C-18C57

René Dubos

Of Human
Diversity

Clark University Press
with Barre Publishers
Distributed by Crown Publishers, Inc., New York
1974

Contents

The Heinz Werner Lectures

The Heinz Werner
Lecture Series

This is the seventh of The Heinz Werner Lecture Series. This series is designed to provide a forum for outstanding scholars who are known for their contributions to the developmental analysis of biological, psychological and/or socio-cultural phenomena. This Series is sponsored by the Heinz Werner Institute of Developmental Psychology.

Heinz Werner (1890-1964) was one of the leading psychologists of the past half century. Deeply impressed by processes of organic formation and ordered change in various domains of the life sciences, he sought to apply developmental conceptualization and developmental analysis to all aspects of existence in which mentality is manifested. Convinced that developmental psychology is not merely a subject matter but is, rather, a manner of conceptualizing all psychological phenomena, Werner sought to encompass animal behavior, ontogenesis, pathological phenomena, products of collective activity, and behavior evoked in experimental situations, within a comprehensive system — a general psychology, grounded in the fundamental concept of development. In accord with Werner's philosophy, the Heinz Werner Institute of Developmental Psychology is devoted to the application of developmental analysis to all psycho-biological and psycho-cultural phenomena. It seeks to fulfill Werner's vision by promoting research and teaching at graduate and post-graduate levels which will serve to integrate the various life sciences without collapsing their distinctiveness in method and subject matter.

Bernard Kaplan
Seymour Wapner

I. NATIONAL INDIVIDUALISM

One blessing which is also a weakness of modern life is the possibility to travel over most of the earth without ever having to change one's habits. In any country there are at least several places where one can start the day with ham and eggs for breakfast, get current quotations on the stock market, dictate letters to a mini-skirted secretary in an air-conditioned office, play a game of tennis or golf, buy souvenirs made in Hong Kong, have a roast beef dinner with French wine, and end the day with a Scotch highball while hearing about Women's Liberation, the Vietnam war, or Picasso's latest fantasies from people who have read *Time* or *The Reader's Digest*. And from almost any part of the globe, one can start the trip back home in full confidence that, within a hundred miles, there will be jet planes staffed by polyglot hostesses serving international foods, drinks, and cigarettes — with international smiles.

Seen from the angles of the globetrotter and of the international businessman or scholar, the earth seems indeed to have become a global village unified by electronics. Much of it appears to have been transformed into environments which are so much alike that they are almost interchangeable. Almost everywhere buildings are designed as if they were to be used as disposable cubicles for dispensable people. But in fact this homogenization of the earth has not reached as deeply or as widely as is commonly stated. Admittedly, technological civilization has modified the external environment, but I doubt that it has altered profoundly the vital aspects of existence. Men and women, young and old, are now moved as much as in the past by the passions, the loves, and the hates which motivated Homer's heroes and make his tales still meaningful to us. People enjoy singing, dancing, or story telling as much as ever. Despite scientific technology, the modern world still derives its color from art, music, fiction, and poetry — and other purely human activities with a strong local character.

International sociologists and hasty globetrotters have of course good reasons to be impressed by the standardization of the world, but they are wrong in assuming that their experiences as scholars and travelers are everyone else's experience of daily life. In reality, few are the people who live, or want to live, in the global village of the international set. The man in the street is eager to use international technology and its products, but in his own individual ways and to his own local needs. Television sets are much the same all over the world, but the love songs and the expressions of the singers are very different in Athens from what they are in Stockholm. And the difference is even greater between Jersey City and Guatemala City.

Scientists tend to be most interested in those aspects of human life which fit the global village because these

8

aspects provide them with convenient material for the discovery of general laws about mankind; the trend toward uniformity gives them an excuse for ignoring the "particulars" of life which interfere with scientific generalizations. Diversity, however, is more important than uniformity in human life because it provides the stuff out of which people create what they cherish most, namely their individualism. And unfortunately, the discovery of universals is rarely of much help in accounting for individual differences.

Among primitive people, individualism manifests itself most clearly in the collective spirit of the tribe. Although modern anthropologists tend to question the validity of the concept tribe,[1] I shall use the word nevertheless to denote a small social group which derives a distinctive individualism from common ancestors, traditions, and sacred places. The unity of the tribe and its distinctive genius are based on a kinship through time and in space originating of course from the simplest links of parentage, but even more from the way its members explain the world to themselves. By accepting tacitly a certain social structure and a body of ancient traditions the members of a particular tribe enjoy the sense of equilibrium and peace that comes from biological continuity and group solidarity. They also have the advantage of knowing who their neighbors are, or better still of not caring who they are because their neighbors are part of their own separate bio-social unity.

According to some anthropologists, the members of a primitive tribe do not have a well-developed sense of individualism. Their thinking and their activities are

9

governed less by personal choices than by unconscious allegiance to the clan and acceptance of its laws. But their tribal individualism is highly developed and they feel intensely different from people of other tribes; they fear the "stranger" because they do not understand his ways and therefore do not know what to expect of him.

Tribal identity is the closest social unity, and also the most enduring, the human race has ever known. As a social form, tribalism lasted more than a hundred thousand years. Its stability is in part biologically determined, but it is based even more on explanations of the meaning of life peculiar to each tribe and accepted by all its members. The beliefs of the yam diggers are different from those of the caribou hunters or of the salmon fishermen because each of these different occupations generates special attitudes toward the place in which it is carried out and toward the cosmic forces that govern the life of the group.[2] The different tribal groups, furthermore, tend to retain their respective beliefs essentially unchanged as long as their traditional ways of life are not profoundly disturbed.

Primitive tribalism has no chance of survival in the modern world because environmental and social conditions are changing everywhere, in Africa as well as in Polynesia. But the need for individualism has not disappeared and indeed seems to become stronger with time. In fact it has evolved into several different directions. The most obvious change from the tribal ways is the cult of personality which makes the individual person the center of the value system. I shall discuss this aspect of human diversity in the following lecture. But on the other hand, there is a harking back to some form of collective unity, a hankering for the sense of coziness associated with belonging to a group.

The manifestations of diversity thus range over a wide spectrum from personal individualism to the individualism of social groups, cities, regions, nations. I shall emphasize the national kind of individualism, precisely because it is the most extreme and distorted contemporary expression of tribalism, including as it does contempt for the alien. Because the alien — the stranger — has habits which are unfamiliar and therefore threatening, he elicits, as in the past, irrational responses which commonly evolve into international violence.

All men, irrespective of color and creed, originate from the same stock, far back in the Old Stone Age. Although the various members of the human species have developed minor genetic differences as a consequence of their migrations over the globe, and of their different ways of life under different environmental conditions, they all continue to share the same anatomical structures, physiological attributes, and psychological drives. This fundamental biological unity of mankind has not prevented, however, the emergence of an immense diversity of social organizations and cultural values. Existential diversity results from the interplay of different human attributes with the immense variety of circumstances men encounter during their daily lives. In other words, men are essentially identical in biological equipment, but they exhibit distinctive characteristics as a result of the diversity of their physical

11

environments, their social institutions, their past experiences and last, but not least, their aspirations. Nationalities are the outcomes of the historical accidents which have caused certain human groups in a certain area to be conditioned for long periods of time by a certain set of environmental and social forces.

At the end of the two World Wars, nationalism was discredited and almost rejected for being an irrational and destructive force responsible for the world's greatest tragedies. There is furthermore a widespread feeling that nationalism has now been rendered obsolete as a form of government by international technology. But while it is true that nationalism is in retreat as an intellectual concept, nations remain vigorous living organisms. They survive and indeed continue to play an essential role probably because they cater to the fundamental human need for kinship that used to be satisfied by the tribal system. Before attempting to identify the processes which account for the persistence of nations, it seems worth illustrating, by a few examples, that national characteristics resist the impact of even the most unifying technologies.

No human activity is more standardized and apparently more independent of national customs than is international air travel. Yet all international airports retain an intensely national flavor. New York, London, Paris are served by the same kinds of aircraft operated according to the same rules; yet a blind and deaf man could perceive the differences in human atmosphere between JFK, Heathrow, and Orly. In each one of these international airports, the national conditioning of the pre-aviation era is reflected in the organization of passenger facilities, the design of announcements and advertisements, the voices and attitudes of the local public.

The human differences are even more striking when one compares airports in the various Pacific islands. These islands have much in common by way of climate, topography, natural resources and colonial history; they are now all populated by a great mixture of people consisting chiefly of Polynesians, Malaysians, Orientals, and Caucasians. But despite this geographical and ethnic similarity, despite also the technological uniformity of international air travel, the airports in the capital cities of Hawaii, Fiji, and Tahiti differ profoundly in human atmosphere. In this case, it is easy to perceive that the differences originate from patterns of behavior influenced respectively by the political domination of the United States, Great Britain, and France. The national distinctiveness of these three countries thus persists even when their people move into environments which differ both physically and socially from those of their origin.

The obvious behavioral differences exhibited by the United States, England, and France are the more surprising in view of the fact that these three countries are made up of essentially the same racial mixtures, have always had intimate cultural and economic contacts, and have long been influenced by the same scientific technology.

The examples of regional differences which I have just quoted illustrate a paradox inherent in man's nature, namely the coexistence of the biological uniformity of mankind and the social diversity of human life. While biological uniformity can be simply explained by the fact that all men derive from a common origin, social diversity is far more difficult to account for because it is the product of multiple and obscure forces. All these forces, furthermore, are interrelated and it is only for the convenience of presentation that I shall consider them separately under different headings corresponding to physical, biological, and social mechanisms.

The shaping of biological characteristics, behavioral patterns, attitudes and tastes by regional influences had been clearly recognized by the Greeks 2500 years ago. In his essay, "Of Airs, Waters, and Places," the physician Hippocrates explicity stated that the physical and mental characteristics of the various populations of Europe and Asia, as well as their military prowess and political institutions, are determined by the topography of the land, the quality of the air and the water, and the abundance and nature of the food. "Inhabitants of mountainous, rocky, well-watered country at a high altitude, where the margin of seasonal climatic variation is wide, will tend to have large-built bodies constitutionally adapted for courage and endurance, and in such natures there will be a considerable element of ferocity and brutality. Inhabitants of sultry hollows covered with water-meadows, who are more commonly exposed to warm winds than to cold and who drink tepid water, will, in contrast, not be large-built or slim, but thickset, fleshy and dark-haired, with swarthy rather than fair complexions and with less phlegm than bile in their constitutions." [3]

Ever since Hippocrates the theory that human traits and therefore national characteristics are shaped by climatic factors has continued to be popular in the countries of Western civilization. One of its most articulate exponents during the eighteenth century was the Abbé Jean-Baptiste DuBos who emphasized the effects of weather on human development and particuuarly on the emergence and expressions of genius in the different parts of the world. As the Abbé DuBos stated in his book *Réflections sur la poésie et la peinture*, "Le climat est plus puissant que le sang et l'origine" (climate is more powerful than blood and origin). And he illustrated this thesis by many historical examples, such as the fact that the Franks who had settled in the Holy Land and adopted the easy ways of southern countries became "effeminate, treacherous, and pusillanimous" after a few generations. He also quoted with approval the statement by Bernard de Fontenelle that,

Different ideas are like plants or flowers which do not thrive equally well in all sorts of climates. Perhaps our French soil is not suited to the Egyptian manner of thinking any more than to their palm trees; and without going so far afield, perhaps the orange trees, which do not thrive so well here as in Italy, are an indication that in Italy there is a certain turn of thought which is not exactly duplicated in France. It is certain, at least, that, because of the connection and inter-independence existing between all parts of the material world, the differences in climate which affect plants must needs influence brains also. [4]

In brief, DuBos believed that the quality of the air influences the composition of the blood and thereby

15

the conformation of the body and the functions of the mind. In his opinion, this accounted for the fact that "arts arise spontaneously under the climates suitable to them" and that various artistic forms achieve their highest level in Europe and tend to degenerate as they are removed from that continent. DuBos, however, was willing to acknowledge that only environmental extremes are incompatible with great human achievements.

The climate theory of human traits and performance is no longer as popular today as it used to be among biologists, physicians, and sociologists. But it has nevertheless persisted into our times in a slightly different form. There are claims, for example, that human activity, both physical and mental, is greatest in areas of pronounced seasonal changes, and where the variations in temperature, sunlight, wind velocity and barometric pressure are sufficient to provide a stimulating but not overpowering environment. E. Huntington, formerly professor of geography at Yale University, believed that eastern New England has just the right level of climatic variability to provide a challenging climate ideal for the development of civilization.[5] As I shall point out later, the view that climatic variability stimulates human achievement can be regarded as a special aspect of Toynbee's "challenge and response" theory of civilization.

Students of man's response to climate have naturally focused their attention on those factors which can be readily measured and which have unequivocal physiological effects — such as temperature, humidity, barometric pressure, gaseous composition of the air. But it is certain that other more subtle factors also influence man's nature and fate. Cosmic rhythms, ionic concentration, the ill-understood influence of certain types of wind are but a few of the environmental forces which are certainly of importance for human welfare and which influence in particular the type of behavior characteristic of a geographical region.[6] Sanitation may be deplorable in Greece and plumbing defective in the south of France, but this counts for little compared with the fact that the scenery, the skies, and the waters of the Mediterranean world engender tastes and attitudes which persist through life.

Nutritional habits, prevailing patterns of infection, and the kinds of stimuli that pervade a particular community are examples of the kinds of biological factors which profoundly influence the biological and psychological characteristics of a group at a given time. As R. W. Emerson wrote in his essay "On the Uses of Great Men," "There are vices and follies incident to whole populations and ages. Men resemble their contemporaries even more than their progenitors." The Arab proverb, "Men resemble their own times more than they do their father"[7] similarly expresses the biological truth that physical, mental and behavioral traits are profoundly affected by surroundings and events.

We resemble our progenitors because we derive from them our genetic constitution. But we usually resemble our contemporaries even more, because we share the same environment, and therefore are exposed to the same conditions during critical phases of life. It is well known that during the past few decades the maturation of young people has greatly accelerated. This change in growth pattern is just as striking among Orientals as among Occidentals. The Japanese used to be thought of as a small race, but now many of their teenagers are almost as tall as Americans of the same age, not because of any change in the genetic constitution of the Japanese people, but because of the new ways of life in postwar Japan. A similar phenomenon has occurred in Israel's kibbutzim. The kibbutzim children, raised under favorable conditions, now tower over their parents who originated from the crowded and unsanitary European ghettos.

The acceleration of growth among the children of Japan and Israel is typical of what has happened in all the countries which have adopted the ways of life of Western civilization. Not only is growth accelerated; final adult heights and weights also are now greater and are achieved earlier in life. A century ago, maximum stature was not reached, in general, until age twenty-nine, whereas it is now reached at about nineteen in boys and seventeen in girls. Sexual maturation is also advanced. Whereas the mean age of menarche was around seventeen in 1850, it is now around twelve in many affluent countries.

The factors responsible for the dramatic changes now being observed in the rate of physical and sexual maturation are not completely understood. Improvements in nutrition and in the control of infections of the mother and the child have certainly played a large part in the acceleration of development during early childhood, and this change in turn has been responsible for the larger size achieved by adults. There is some evidence also that greater ease of communication and thereby wider range in the choice of a mate has resulted in hybrid vigor.

Genetic factors of this nature may have played a role in some striking anatomical changes which occured in Europe during the early Middle Ages. Before and throughout Roman times, there had been large movements of population which had encouraged matings between various groups. In contrast, medieval serfs did not marry outside their villages, the consequence being an increase in endogamy resulting in reduced stature and greater brachycephaly.[8] The short, stocky peasant, familiar in Medieval tapestries, would thus be in part an expression of sedentary village life. In contrast, there is a real possibility that the heterosis resulting from the great social mobility in our times accounts in part for the change in biological characteristics that has happened in all Westernized countries.

Although no systematic study has been made of the long-range behavioral consequences of changes in physiological development, it can be assumed that the rate of anatomical and physiological maturation exerts an influence on the ease of finding one's place in the social order of things. More generally it may affect certain psychological attitudes and even the forms of civilization. As the Japanese grow heavier and taller, for example, there will have to be changes in the design of their furniture, buildings and grounds — even in

19

the management of their landscape and in the conduct of their ceremonial life.

As commonly used in the preceding paragraphs, the word *environment* refers to the physical and biological factors ubiquitous in the community. But in addition to the aspects of the environment which are outside of us, in the external world, there are others that exist only in the individual mind and therefore constitute a person's private conceptual environment. The environment of a primitive population living on a Micronesian atoll includes of course the sea, the land, and the sky, but it also includes a host of spirits that lurk everywhere. Although the spirits of the Micronesian conceptual environment do not have concrete existence, they nevertheless affect profoundly the inhabitants of the atoll. They become malevolent when not properly treated and elicit behavioral responses that may be more dangerous than wounds inflicted by sharks or poisonous eels.

Nor is the conceptual environment of less importance in industrial societies. Whether sophisticated and learned, or primitive and ignorant, every human being lives in a conceptual environment of his own which conditions all his ethical and social attitudes, such as his opinions concerning the nature of progress, his view of man's place in the cosmic order of things, the attributes that he associates with the word *God*.

The contrast in attitude between Athens and Sparta in classical Greece obviously transcends conventional explanation in terms of race, climate, or topography; economic explanations also fail to account for the differences. In fact, the very concepts of city-state and nation-state emerged not from natural necessities, but from human imagination.

Environmental effects on the shaping of national individuality are greatly complicated by man's tendency to symbolize everything that he experiences. In most cases, furthermore, the person does not create the symbols to which he responds. He receives most of the elements of his symbolic system from the group of which he is a member. His views of the physical and social universe are impressed upon him very early in life by ritual and myth, taboos and parental training, traditions and education. These acquired attitudes constitute the basic premises according to which he organizes his inner and outer worlds. The process of socialization, which is essential to human existence, consists precisely in the acquirement of these collective symbols with all their associated values.

The symbolic system differs profoundly from culture to culture, but it can persist essentially unchanged for many generations within one given culture. In such a stable system, the person's views of the total universe are transmitted as a social heritage through the same kind of mechanisms that operate for other early influences; furthermore, they are not subject to question. This stability of the symbolic system minimizes individual differences and thus gives greater homogeneity to the group.

At the end of the seventeenth century Bernard de Fontenelle had clearly recognized the role of social forces (which he called *moral qualities*) in shaping national characteristics. As already mentioned, he had stated that since the orange trees do not grow as well in France as in Italy, it could be surmised that there existed in Italy "a certain turn of thought not exactly duplicated in France." But he went on to say also that "art and culture can exercise a much greater influence upon brains than upon the soil, which is of a harder and more intractable nature. Hence the thoughts of one country are more readily conveyed to another than are plants, and we should experience less difficulty in adopting the Italian genius in our works than in raising orange trees." [9] He had recognized, in other words, that social conditioning is at least as powerful as physical and biological forces in shaping the genius of a region or a nation.

Few people now believe the Hitlerian doctrine that nations are based on race or on a *Verbundenheit mit dem Boden* — a rootedness in the soil. Whatever its precise origin, nationalism is first and foremost a state of mind, an act of consciousness based on a community of past experiences and of present interests. In every society, there is a convention of vision and perhaps of each of the senses. "If Homeric Greek makes no distinction between blue and green, can we be sure those less blind than Homer were able to see the difference." Americans are even more disturbed by horse meat than the French are by cornbread.[10]

In practice most of the members of a given society want to act as they are expected to act. In other words, they desire what is socially desirable and strive to achieve their particular culture's definition of the good

22

life, because they are conditioned to find it personally rewarding.

In his essay "The English People" George Orwell asks rhetorically: "Do such things as national cultures really exist?" To which he answers that this is one of those questions in which scientific arguments are on one side and instinctive knowledge on the other. As I have said, there is no reason to believe that all members of a nation share some mystical quality derived from blood relationships or from the land on which they live. But, just the same, common sense leaves no doubt that a distinctive array of intellectual and behavioral attributes is associated with the adjectives *American, British, French, German, Greek, Italian,* or *Spanish* even more than with the adjectives *Nordic* and *Mediterranean.* Likewise, the words *Chinese* and *Japanese* denote attitudes that have remained different for many centuries regardless of social regime and military conquest. Nations exist not as geological, climatic, or racial entities, but as human experiences. The American social critic Max Lerner was not entirely facetious when he illustrated the use of the two words *permitted* and *forbidden* in different European countries. "In England, everything that is not forbidden is permitted. In Germany everything is forbidden unless it is permitted. In France everything is permitted even if it is forbidden. And in Russia everything is forbidden even if it is permitted." [11]

Modern historical knowledge has confirmed that groups of people whom the accidents of history force to live together in a certain place tend to develop a body of shared ideas, values, and beliefs, which progressively becomes their ideal and guide. The culture they develop constitutes a whole which shapes itself as a continuously evolving national spirit. Order is not imposed on the national genius from the outside; it evolves spontaneously as a structure of interrelationships generated by the constant interplay of its various elements. In this light, national characteristics are the expressions, not of race or other biological properties, but of human choices based on the collective acceptance of certain conventions and traditions — and perhaps especially of myths. In "The English People," Orwell asserted that "myths which are believed in tend to become true because they set up a type of 'persona' which the average person will do his best to resemble." For example, the behavior of the British population during the Second World War "was partly due to the existence of the national 'persona' — that is, to their preconceived idea of themselves." Nations need heroes to symbolize their genius and serve as models of behavior.

The tastes, attitudes, and behavioral patterns which characterize the people of a particular nation endure because they are acquired during the formative years of childhood and early adulthood. This does not mean, however, that they are unchangeable. The ascetic and warlike Moslems who conquered southern Spain in the eighth century progressively lost their military stamina as they adopted the Andalusian ways of life; there is little in common between Mohammed's tent and the Alhambra in Granada, yet the spread in time is only a few centuries. The uncouth and redoubtable Norman barons of the early medieval period built huge fortresses to dominate the French countryside, but their castles were infiltrated by troubadours from the south who brought with them the cult of woman and the courts of love, thereby creating the somewhat effeminate atmosphere of late Gothic life.

It is now common knowledge that the Bolshevik regime, despite its claims to internationalism, was from the beginning and has remained intensely national. As early as the mid-1920s it had developed a "deep concern for the early masters of Russian literature;" the leading writers of the time "following Lenin's precepts, regarded the cultural values of the past as the foundation of the culture of the future." This fundamentally national attitude had deep roots in the Russian tradition.[12]

At the end of his life of exile in Paris, Turgenev for example used to speak of the "deep unfathomable chasm" between the Russian conception of social problems and the views held on the same subject by French, English, German, and other Europeans. Even the revolutionary aristocrat Peter Kropotkin, who had long affirmed that these differences of view existed only among the middle classes of the various nations, came to realize that the workers also saw things in quite different ways, depending upon their nationality.

The concern for the quality of Russianness which inspires almost all Russian writers has been most remarkably expressed by the Nobel Prize winner Solzhenitsyn, even though he has been discredited by the Kremlin for his political views. In the first chapter of his novel *August 1914* Solzhenitsyn presents Russian nationalism not as an idea but as an affective reaction, deeply rooted in the subconscious. Russianness has something to do with the soil, and everything to do with the people, their beliefs, and their language. It is unrelated to political ideologies and is as natural as a tree, deeply rooted in the subsoil of a culture and rising toward the heavens in a desire to transcend the immediate situation.[13] For Solzhenitsyn, Russia is not a place on the map but an image shaped by the Russians — much as for George Orwell England was an attitude formulated by Englishmen.

In fact, a territory once occupied by a given people may be lost by them without causing the breakdown of their national identity. Such persistence of identity is well recognized in the case of the Jews, but it has also been observed in the case of many other people; for example, the Yaquis, the Navajos and the Cherokees who were displaced from all or part of their territories yet survived as a people. National individualism commonly survives political domination also. The Irishmen of the Republic of Ireland feel and express a continuity with the Irishmen of more than 1,000 years ago; even though they eventually became part of Great Britain for a long period of time, they have steadfastly rejected any thought of identification with Englishmen. There is evidence indeed that tragic experiences tend to reinforce the identity of social groups or nations; such experiences help people to maintain their conception of themselves and of their collective identity under a wide range of physical and socio-cultural environments.[14] Except in a limited biological sense, it is not the actual past that shapes the view we have of ourselves and that generates the rules of our behavior; it is rather the image we create of the past.[15]

Aleksandr Blok, who was one of the best known Russian symbolists of the early twentieth century, has tried in *The Collapse of Humanism* to differentiate between civilization and culture. For him, culture is the "musical" reality that underlies everything, the sense of complete harmony between spirit and flesh, man and nature — a truly elemental force. "Great is our elemental memory . . . the musical sounds of our cruel nature have rung in the ears of Gogol, Tolstoy, Dostoevsky."[16] According to Blok, civilization is unconcerned with this musical quality and emphasizes instead material possessions, calendar time, and the growth of specialities even though these characteristics are mutually exclusive. Vague as it is, the distinction between culture and civilization helps one to understand why international technology has not yet destroyed national individualism. It suggests also the nature of the mechanisms which have made the national spirit such a powerful creative force.

Before the advent of man, much of the earth's surface was covered by forests and marshes. There was an overpowering grandeur in this seemingly endless green mantle, but it was a grandeur ill-suited to man's limitations. Furthermore, it masked some of the most interesting aspects of the earth; in many cases the architecture of the landscape was revealed only after the forests had been cleared and the marshes drained.

All over the globe, men have now humanized the land on which they live. The wilderness has been replaced by farmlands, pastures, gardens, parks, which have become so familiar that they are commonly assumed to be of natural origin. But in reality it is man who has created most of the forms of the "nature" loved by common people and celebrated by artists and poets.

In any particular country the appeal of "nature" depends largely upon a *human* quality which transcends physical and ecological considerations. Whatever the characteristics of the natural environment there always emerges a new kind of value from the intimate and long association between man and the landscape. The creation of man-made nature began long ago as a true symbiosis between the ancient peasantry and the land it created from wilderness. This wooing of the earth which has been continued for many centuries calls to mind the Moslem word *báraka* which refers to the sense of blessedness that attaches itself to places and objects after years of loving care. And it is precisely this symbiosis, this wooing of the land through loving care — this *báraka* — which is the creative force out of which national individualism emerged in the course of time."

Countless examples could be quoted to illustrate how national and regional landscapes all over the world have been humanized and have thereby acquired their individualism. But I shall limit myself to the Ile de France, in part because I was born and raised there, and also because this was a region without any notable characteristics before it was transformed by man. The

28

hills have such low profiles that they would be of little interest if it were not for the diversified agriculture they now support, and for the venerable churches and clusters of houses which crown their summits. The rivers tend to be sluggish and the ponds muddy, but their shores have been adapted to human use and are associated with peaceful rural scenes. The sky is rarely spectacular but its soft luminosity gives life to a wide range of plants, many of them introduced by man. Ever since the primeval forest was cleared by Neolithic settlers and medieval farmers, the Ile de France has thus acquired a humanized quality which transcends its natural endowments. To this day, the land has remained fertile, even though it has been in continuous use for more than 2,000 years. Far from being exhausted by intensive agriculture, it still supports a great diversity of human settlements.

What I have just stated about the Ile de France is applicable, as already mentioned, to many other parts of the world. The prodigious labors of settlers and farmers have generated an astonishing diversity of ecosystems which appear natural even though they are of human origin. From Japan to Italy, from China to Holland, from Java to Sweden civilizations have thus been built on a variety of ecosystems which are almost completely man-made, and which derive their distinctiveness from symbiotic relationships with human beings. For example, there is much climatic and geologic similarity betwen England and northern France, yet the landscapes in these two countries have become different because they have been influenced for centuries by contrasting social and political forces.

Around the Puget Sound, the cities of Seattle in the United States and Victoria in British Columbia have also evolved in a different manner, despite their ecological similarities, because they have been populated by different kinds of people. As already mentioned, the Pacific Islands have acquired distinctive individualities which derive in part from the characteristics of the Western countries which have most influenced their economic and social development. Even more spectacular are the expressions of social conditioning in the American Southwest. There, five entirely different cultures with completely different types of relation to the land coexist at the present time: the Zunis, the Navajos, the Mormons, the Catholic Mexicans, and the Texas rangers. One could hardly imagine more contrasting religious attitudes, social philosophies, and ways of life.[18] Yet all these people derive a living from the same kind of land under the same scorching sun, but to the beat of different cultural drums.

There is nothing final about a given landscape. Nature is like a great stream of events which can flow in different directions, at different intensities, depending upon accidental circumstances and especially upon the kind of influences exerted by man. Wherever this influence is intelligently applied in a sound ecological manner, man and nature enter in a symbiotic relationship which modifies both of them, creating thereby the humanized landscapes which characterize each region and each nation. The words *place* and *nation* refer to a fusion of human and natural order. Viewed only as a life-support system, the earth, or any particular place on it, is only a physical environment. In contrast, a place or a nation is a piece of the environment which has been emotionally transformed by feelings.

There are of course many worthwhile expressions of nature which have not been humanized When the flow of natural events is undisturbed it generates a wilderness which commonly far exceeds in beauty and emotional power the landscapes created by man. In our daily life, however, we do not function in the wilderness and are hardly ever passive in front of the natural world. We fence it, manipulate it, and alter it to create environments suited to our limitations and aspirations. By inserting our dreams and our sense of order into ecological determinism, we shape the raw stuff of nature into patterns which incorporate both human nature and the materials provided by the wilderness — a truly creative symbiosis.

Since most present landscapes reflect a certain kind of human intervention, they could be otherwise than they are; but as already pointed out, this does not mean that they could be anything at all. To be viable, humanized nature must be compatible with ecological constraints. What is certain, however, is that a given landscape and an established society are usually the products of a long process of adaptation, the ultimate result being that the society makes the environment a dimension of itself. If a people live in a place long enough, the quality of the place enters into the substance of their life.[19]

I have purposefully used the word *symbiosis* repeatedly to emphasize that the relationships between landscape and man are essentially biological in nature and bring about a creative change in both components of the system. But I have also indicated that there commonly is an element of conscious choice in the type of order man inserts into natural systems. I shall mention again in the following lecture man's ability to choose, eliminate, and thereby create his own selected ways of life. At this point I wish only to state that social groups, like individual persons, never *react* passively with environmental situations; instead they *respond* in a purposive manner.

It has long been recognized, as mentioned earlier, that the growth of civilization is favored by variable and challenging environments — whether the challenge comes from topographic, climatic, or social stimuli. But civilizations do not emerge from the passive reactions of the social group to these stimuli; to repeat, they are the expressions of purposive responses made in an attempt to reach some selected goal. It is this active, creative aspect of the interplay between man and his total environment which gives such a rich meaning to Toynbee's famous formulation of history: "challenge and response."

Although the group may respond as a whole, most far-reaching historical movements can be traced to one particular person, or more precisely to a view of the world perceived or imagined by that person. It is the fact that a given person did something or took a certain stand at a given time — that Washington beat Cornwallis at Yorktown, or that Lincoln made slavery a dominant political issue — and not the probabilities that those events could occur under a given set of circumstances, which radically affects the subsequent course of history.

The uniqueness of an initial visionary concept of a given course of action explains why natural sciences have contributed so little to the prediction or even the explanation of great historical events. The scientific method has been designed to deal with phenomena which can be repeated at will or manipulated by experimentation and therefore is of little use for the study of unique events. There were certainly "reasons" for the explosive growth of Islamic civilization during the early Middle Ages; but Islam as a political force was born unpredictably in the mind of Mohammed — a small Mecca merchant who belonged to a poor and almost illiterate tribe having little contact with the outside world. There were also good historical and economic "reasons" for the Crusades, but the crucial idea of the first Crusade was born in the mind of Peter the Hermit, a monk with an obsessive concern for the fate of the Holy Land. And much the same could be said of course for all the great historical and social movements of modern times. There are always "reasons" for these movements, but leaders accelerate or even generate them, and they impose on them certain directions and patterns. Whereas biological evolution is Darwinian in that it involves only causes — not purpose — social evolution is Lamarckian in that it makes use of acquired characters and is deeply influenced by conscious purpose.

The colonial wars and the social revolutions of our times have demonstrated that technological power is no match for human will. But since human will always implies individual persons, national individualism is, in the final analysis, an expression of personal individualism.

II. PERSONAL INDIVIDUALISM

The words *individualism* and *personality* are often used as if they had exactly the same meaning and were interchangeable. Yet they are etymologically different and their differences in etymology are important because they referred initially to different kinds of forces acting on the human organism.

The word *individualism* has the same root as *indivisible*. It implies that the biological organization of a given living thing — microbe, plant, animal or man — is so tightly integrated that any profound disturbance in any of its component parts is likely to affect the health and even the viability of the whole organism. The highly integrated biological organization of any living thing and its distinctive biological characteristics are the phenotypic expressions of the interplay between its genetic apparatus and environment conditions. They are the results of purely biological forces.

The Latin word *persona* seems to be derived from an Etruscan word meaning mask. In archaic societies a mask (or a costume) was placed on a particular human being to indicate his place or function in the group. This disguise changed the place of the person in society — without changing him biologically. It would seem best therefore to use the word *personality* for those attributes and attitudes which are acquired socially by the human being as a result of either his own choice or of decisions by his group.

I shall in this essay keep in mind the etymologies outlined in the preceding paragraphs, although, as I shall point out later, the constant interplay between biological and social forces makes it impossible in practice to establish a clear-cut separation between individualism and personality. In an arbitrary manner, I shall for the time being define *individualism* as what the human being becomes through the operation of blind biological forces, and *personality* as what he tries to be, or is made to be, chiefly through conscious social choices. In the light of this definition, to be a person means wearing a mask over one's biological nature in order to act a certain social role.

Individualism being a purely biological attribute exists in very primitive human societies and in all animal societies as well. Since no two human beings are identical, each has a biological individualism; but many anthropologists believe that this biological distinctiveness is of minor importance in primitive tribes. As mentioned in the preceding lecture, primitive man is completely identified with his tribe, unconsciously obeys its laws, and hardly ever acts independently. Each tribal member is somewhat different from his companions but he is fundamentally an anonymous part of a gregarious community to which he belongs, without any deliberate prior choice either on his part or on that of the group. Even today, when a word corresponding to our *I* occurs in the language of a primitive tribe, it often has the extended meaning of *we*. For example a Maori, when speaking in the first person, does not necessarily refer to himself, but instead to his group or tribe as a whole.[1]

Primitive man achieved the state of a real person — in the sense adopted in this essay — only after he separated himself in some way from the anonymity of the tribe, or was separated from it either by accident or coercion. In a pre-agricultural tribe the hunter considers himself part of the natural order of things and is likely to choose the community's decision over his own self-interest. After the domestication of plants and animals, however, the ethos of the hunter progressively gave way to the ethos of the peasant. The emphasis on personal individualism, competition, hierarchies, savings and ownership, which are regarded as characteristics of modern life, in reality originated from the peasant ethos.[2] And mankind has been ever since traveling on a road of ever increasing individual consciousness from which there seems to be no return.

It is probable that being cut off from the clan or becoming differentiated from it generated in primitive man some form of existential anxiety. As recognized by the theologian Duns Scotus in the fourteenth century, "Personality is the ultimate solitude." [3] The reason our period has been called the age of anxiety may be in part that the eagerness to achieve personal individualism has become extremely widespread. The anxiety of isolation has never been more strongly expressed than by Maxim Gorky in *The Confession:* "This vile life, unworthy of human reason, began on that day when the first individual tore himself away from the miraculous strength of the people, from the masses, from his mother, and frightened by his isolation and his weakness, pitied himself and grew to be a futile and evil master of petty desires, a mass which called itself 'I'. It is this same 'I' which is the worst enemy of man." [4]

One of the expressions of personal individualism in our times is the hipster's emphasis on the self, his desire to consider himself the center of the universe rather than the product of anonymous biochemical mechanisms and social forces. In the words of Norman Mailer, the hipster's ideal is "to exist without roots, to be set out on that uncharted journey into the rebellious imperatives of the self." [5]

Although the attributes of the organism that I have designated by the words *individualism* and *personality* have different origins, in practice they constantly interplay and merge into each other. The integrated biological characteristics which constitute individualism affect in a decisive manner the acquisition or selection by a particular human being of his place and role in the social group and thus contribute to the development of his personality. On the other hand, the acquisition of personality, whether deliberately assumed or given by society, exposes the person to certain environments and experiences which influence his further development, thereby causing irreversible changes in his biological individualism. This constant interplay between individualism and personality is the mechanism of existential expression at every moment of life. Thus

38

individualism and personality differ in origin but become less distinguishable with time because they interplay at all stages of life.

Biological uniqueness (individualism) has genetic determinants. Except for identical twins, no two human beings inherit the same array of genes. Furthermore, the statistical chance is practically nil that the genetic constitution of anyone living now has ever occurred in the past, or will ever occur again in the future. But biological uniqueness also results from the unique constellation of surroundings and events that influence development. Most of the stimuli that impinge on a human being leave on him a stamp which cannot be eradicated and which affects all his subsequent responses to other stimuli. Behavioral patterns and emotional attitudes, just like immunities and allergies, can be regarded as different forms of biological memory which persist throughout the whole life span. Each human being is unique, unprecedented, and unrepeatable.

Conditioning by the environment begins during the intrauterine life. Even though the Dionne quintuplets were genetically identical, they could be differentiated by their attendants from the time of birth, and their biological and mental individualities became increasingly different as they grew older It is probable that the relative position of the five fetuses in the uterus created for each of them slightly different environmental conditions at critical stages of their development, thus resulting in phenotypic distinctiveness. Prenatal influences — as exerted for example by nutritional and hormonal factors, as well as by drugs and infectious agents — exert on the fetus profound effects that persist after birth and throughout life. And this is the reason why genetic identity does not prevent phenotypic diversity.

As commonly used, the phrase *early influences* denotes the conditioning of behavioral and emotional characteristics by the forces that impinge on the newborn baby and on the child during the formative stages of development, for example as a result of parental child-rearing practices. Many other kinds of environmental forces, however, also play important roles in shaping individuality by acting on it during early life and thus imposing directions and limitations on subsequent development. From topography of the environment to climatic factors, from nutrition to education, from sensory stimuli to religious beliefs, the types of influences that leave a permanent stamp on the organism are countless.[6]

Early experiences do more than condition behavioral patterns and emotional attitudes. They also affect profoundly and lastingly such purely biological characteristics as initial growth rate, efficiency in the utilization of food, anatomical structures, physiological attributes, maximum adult size, response to various forms of stresses and stimuli, in brief almost every phenotypic expression of the adult. This aspect of early biological conditioning has been illustrated in the first lecture by the anatomical, physiological, and behavioral changes that have occurred among Japanese and Jews since the end of the Second World War. But I shall document it somewhat further at this time with examples illustrating that the very way we perceive the world is profoundly conditioned by early experiences.

The classical behaviorists (Pavlov, Watson) believed that the brain has almost unlimited adaptation capability; many surgeons also tended at that time to assume that functional readjustment would restore proper functions to disarranged structures almost automatically; the motto was "let function do it." [7] But in fact, the plasticity of the brain has its limitations. The nerve cells acquire individual identification tags very early in the course of development; they establish lasting functional hookups only with cells to which the growing fibers are selectively matched. One of the reasons the first years are so influential is that the preprogrammed maturational processes unfold with the greatest rapidity at that time.

Despite the extensive preprogramming of the brain, however, almost any form of experience engenders in its structures anatomical as well as chemical changes. Such changes continue to occur during the whole life span, but they are most profound and frequent during the early years. [8]

Recent neurobiological studies have provided striking evidence of the plasticity of the vertebrate brain. For example, experiments have revealed that the early visual experiences of kittens influence their visual performance later in life; furthermore, observations indicate that the same is true for human beings. What seems to happen is that the wiring between the eyes and the visual centers of the brain is organized by what is seen

41

— i.e., the visual inputs — during an early critical phase of development.

Kittens were reared from two weeks to five months of age in cages where they saw horizontal or vertical lines, but not both. When the *horizontally-experienced* kittens were set free in a normal environment they could see horizontal lines but were blind to vertical components or objects. The *vertically-experienced* kittens had a similar visual deficiency but in the opposite direction. In both cases, the partial blindness was practically irreversible because each animal's cortex had become wired up to cope with visual inputs that were interpreted as normal.[9]

In human beings with astigmatism, the optical system of the eye similarly gets distorted so that objects are in focus in one plane, horizontal for example, but are out of focus in the vertical plane. Like the kittens, astigmatic people see lines mainly in one direction only. Even when the astigmatism is corrected with the proper glasses, the affected individuals are still almost blind in one plane; the lines fall in perfect focus on their retina, but their nerve connections are unable to make use of them. Since the human visual system is probably in its critical period of development during the first five or six years of life, it is essential to correct as early as possible visual defects that might leave a permanent deficiency, but the trouble is that astigmatism is not readily detected in very young children.

Granted that early influences — both prenatal and postnatal — play a dominant role in converting genetic potentialities into biological and mental attributes, it is also true that surroundings and events continue to have formative effects on the adult throughout his life span. Responses made by the adult organism to environmental stimuli do become inscribed in the body and the mind, thereby altering subsequent responses to the same and other stimuli. As Katzantzakis says of Ulysses, "Your voyages have been your native land." [10] Throughout our lives, we are imprinted by what we *really* experience. I have emphasized the word *really* because as already mentioned we do not experience all the stimuli to which we are exposed. At any given phase of our life, our perceptual environment is not identical with the external environment; we deal with the past not through what it has actually been, but with the traces it has left in us.

Individualism reflects, therefore, the evolutionary past as encoded in the genetic apparatus and the experiential past as inscribed in the bodily structures that store biological and mental memories. Since what we are at any given time includes all the inherited potentialities that have been made functional by life experiences, and since we continually change in response to environmental stimuli, individualism might be defined as the evolving phenotype. Individualism incarnates all aspects of the evolutionary and the experiential past.

As illustrated in the preceding sections, the array of genes we inherit does not determine rigidly the kind of person we become. We are born so to speak with a kit of tools rather than as a working machine. Or to change the image, we are born with the capacity of being a hundred different persons, but in fact become only one of them or at most two or three. What we become is of course profoundly influenced by forces beyond our control — our heredity and accidental circumstances — but most human beings believe that they have nevertheless some measure of freedom in controlling their evolution and their fate. Normal and healthy human beings believe in free will.

Although the awareness of freedom in making decisions and choices is a straightforward experience, it appears incompatible with the deterministic view of behavior and development which has been discussed in the preceding section. In fact, when the process of decision making is analyzed in all its details, step-by-step, freedom seems to disappear because all aspects of behavior are found to be under the control of genetic, experiential, and environmental factors.

It is extremely difficult if not impossible to devise a theoretical formulation encompassing both determinism and freedom, but this difficulty is not a valid argument against the existence of free will. In any field of science, many ill-understood phenomena and entities are not readily explainable in terms of the concepts derived from deterministic studies of simpler or more restricted systems. Light cannot be understood by regarding it merely as a stream of particles moving in accordance with the classical laws of mechanics. Similarly, it is improbable that the experience of free will can be explained by the contemporary concepts of physics, chemistry, and natural selection which are used to account for deterministic biological phenomena.

44

Niels Bohr saw in the determinism-freedom polarity a biological manifestation of the *complementarity* principle he had formulated for subatomic processes. Just as physicists study the electron either as a wave or as a particle depending upon the conditions under which observations are made, so Bohr suggested human behavior should be studied either as a manifestation of free will or of determinism, depending upon the point of view of the observer. In the present essay, I shall accept free will as a needed and useful belief (even though I do not know how to account for it) simply because I consider that the direct experience of freedom is more impressive than the failure to prove its existence by theoretical arguments.

Operationally, the manifestations of free will can readily be recognized. All observers of animal life acknowledge the impossibility of predicting the behavior of a given animal in a given situation. Pavlov himself had emphasized that even his best-conditioned dogs often failed to behave according to prediction. This unpredictability of response led an exasperated physiologist to state what has come to be known as The Harvard Law of Animal Behavior: "Under precisely controlled conditions, an animal does as he damn pleases." The same law certainly applies with even greater strength to most human beings, even during childhood.

From the very beginning of his life, the human child is aware of his environment, stores information about it, and develops certain patterns of responses to it. Even early in life, man (like other mammals) is an active, searching participant in the learning process rather than just a passive receiver. The early phase of biological maturation is followed by a more active and conscious one during which the child appears to create his *self* by making use of his genetic endowment and early experiences.

In mid-childhood — perhaps after the age of five — the child tries to *imagine* a world of his own in which he can act out his individuality from the information and patterns of responses he has already acquired. I have used here the word *imagine* in the strong etymological sense given it by Shelley in *Defence of Poetry*: "We want the creative faculty to imagine (i.e., create an image of) that which we know." Much of subsequent life consists in the unfolding of the behavioral patterns that are elicited by this *imagined* world, in which biological constitution, environmental forces, past experiences are inextricably woven with our dreams. Malraux's phrase. "Certains de nos rêves n'ont pas moins de signification que nos souvenirs" (some of our dreams have as much significance for us as our memories)" is as biologically meaningful as it is poetically evocative.

An increasing degree of freedom in making decisions is evidence of continuing development in normal human beings. Adult man is par excellence the creature who can eliminate, choose, organize, and thereby create. His individuality becomes richer and more complex as he responds to environmental forces and takes initiatives according to certain values and anticipations of the future that are largely his creations, yet have their roots in his past.

Much of modern existentialist literature is an affirmation of the person's right to affirm his individualism at the moment of action. This right had been proclaimed with passion by many writers of the past century. For example:

Fyodor Dostoevsky: "Man only exists for the purpose of proving to himself that he is a man and not an organstop! He will prove it even if it means physical suffering, even if it means turning his back on civilization." [12]

José Ortega y Gasset: "Living is precisely the inexorable necessity to make oneself determinate, *to enter into an exclusive destiny*, to accept it — that is, to resolve to *be it*. We have, whether we like it or not, to realize our 'personage', (our vocation, our vital program, our 'entelechy') — there is no lack of names for the terrible reality which is our authentic I (ego)." [13]

André Gide: "What could have been said by someone other than you, do not say it; what could have been done by someone other than you, do not do it; of yourself, be interested only in those aspects that do not exist except in you; create out of yourself patiently or impatiently, the most unique and irreplacable of beings." [14]

Paul Tillich: "Individualism is the self-affirmation of the individual self as individual self without regard to its participation in its world." [15]

In the practical experience of daily life, the expressions of individuality reflect a functioning structure made up of inherited and acquired characteristics that are organically integrated. This integrated structure is more or less enduring and remains effective long after the conditions that have brought it into being have disappeared. Subsequent responses to environmental stimuli thus rapidly acquire a certain degree of independence from the evolutionary past and even from the cultural group. Irrespective of theories concerning the ultimate nature of free will, this independence is precisely the attribute that enables man to create a future of his own choice.

By the exercise of free will, man has a certain degree of latitude in moving into certain environments; the ways of life he selects elicit from him in turn responses that become lastingly incorporated in his physical and mental constitution. Equally important is the fact that such choices affect the responses of young people placed in a certain physical and social environment during the formative stages of their life. Each individual choice thus imposes a direction and a pattern on the future development of the social group. In this sense man makes himself, individually and socially, through a continuous series of responsible choices governed by anticipations of the future and by value judgments.

Free will cannot express itself in acts of freedom if there is no chance for choices with regard to courses of action. Whatever their theoretical freedom, for example, slum children are almost denied the chance to actualize their human potentialities because they have so few options to choose from. It is not correct to say that lack of culture determines their behavior. The more painful truth is that they acquire early in life a slum culture from which their chance to escape is very limited. In other words, their early surroundings and ways of life greatly limit the range within which they can manifest their freedom.

In the words of J. B. S. Haldane, "That society enjoys the greatest amount of liberty in which the greatest number of human genotypes can develop their peculiar abilities. It is generally admitted that liberty demands equality of opportunity. It is not equally realized that it demands a variety of opportunities." [16] The phrase "variety of opportunities" is usually given political and sociological connotations, but it should also imply the biological determinants of behavior.

Experiments in animals, and observations in man, have revealed that the development of the brain, of learning ability, and of behavioral attitudes, is conditioned by the metabolic factors that affect anatomical and physiological growth, and by the sensory stimuli to which the organism is exposed. Since latent potentialities can be realized only to the extent that circumstances favor their phenotypic expression, they have a better chance to be activated when the social environment is sufficiently diversified to provide a wide range of stimulating experiences, especially for the young. In this sense, diversity within a given culture is an essential component of true functionalism.

As more and more persons express their natural endowments under a wide variety of conditions, society becomes richer and civilizations continue to unfold. In contrast, if the surroundings and ways of life are highly stereotyped — whether in prosperity or in poverty — the only components of man's nature that flourish are those adapted to the narrow range of prevailing conditions. Hence, we have the dangers of the typical modern housing developments which, although sanitary and comfortable, are designed as if their only function was to provide disposable cubicles for dispensable people.

Irrespective of their genetic constitution and economic status, people raised in a featureless environment, and limited to a narrow range of life experiences, run the danger of being crippled intellectually. For this reason, we must shun uniformity of surroundings as much as absolute conformity in behavior. Creating diversified environments may result in some loss of efficiency; but diversity is vastly more important than efficiency because it is essential to the germination of the seeds dormant in man's nature. Monuments, open spaces such as parks or public stages, are essential to the city, not only for their contribution to health and pleasure, but also because they constitute the environments in which citizens can involve themselves in acting out the myths and rituals of their lives. There must be places where the young can observe the adult ways of life and occupations, where parents can act out for the children the community work patterns, where adolescents can achieve maturity by going through their own rituals. The city and the street should once more become as they were on many occasions in the past, a public theater where art and life are the same, and in which the audience is both actor and spectator.

Ideally, each person and especially each child should

have ready access to settings in which he can act out his life, in his own way. A meadow, an ocean shore, the banks of a river, a peaceful village green, a secluded room, the crowded square of a city, or a busy street displaying the multifarious activities of daily life constitute as many different settings in which different kinds of human acts can be performed. Thinking of my own early life, I realize how much I have benefited from having had the opportunity to select as the stage for my life one or the other of the hundred different atmospheres in streets, parks, and public squares of Paris and Rome. Even though the famous cities of the world are uncomfortable and even traumatic, they continue nevertheless to breed a wide range of talents precisely because they offer a great diversity of stages on which very different kinds of people can act out lives of their own choice. "Variety is not the spice of life; it is the very stuff of it," was the conclusion of Christopher Burney in his account of solitary confinement."

Since surroundings and events play a crucial role in the possibility to exercise freedom, environmental design should provide as wide a range of choices as possible. The word *design* refers here to social planning, urban or rural development, and to all practices that affect the conduct of life. In a larger sense, it also implies values because free will can operate only where there is first some form of conviction. To a large extent values are culturally determined; they are based on prevailing social attitudes as well as on prejudices and on the common sense derived from the experience of daily

51

life. There is also a real possibility that, in the future, values might increasingly originate from the natural and social sciences. While scientific knowledge cannot, per se, define or impose values to govern behavior, it provides a factual basis for option. Choice can thus be made more rational by basing it on information and on evaluation of consequences. But in the final analysis, choice always involves a value judgment. This ambiguous statement constitutes another way of acknowledging the existence of the determinism-freedom polarity which pervades all aspects of the human condition.

Freedom is concerned not only with what to do, but also with what not to do. It is incompatible with complete permissiveness because some form of discipline is essential to the integration of all human as well as animal societies. Total anarchy is unbiological because it would inevitably result in the disintegration of the social order and therefore in the destruction of individual lives. In fact, political philosophies have always tended to oscillate between individual liberty emphasizing the right of the person to behave independently of community mores, and social cohesion based on the belief that the person must be willing to sacrifice himself to the welfare of the group. The broader biological rule is that design, rather than anarchy, is the characteristic of life. In human life, design implies the acceptance and even the deliberate choice of certain constraints which are deterministic to the extent that they incorporate the past and the influences of the environment. But design is also the expression of free will governed by value judgments and anticipations

52

of the future.

Most human beings now live in environments which differ profoundly from those in which the human species acquired its genetic endowment during the Stone Age. And to a certain extent, this is true of many other land mammals. The ability to adapt to new environments, within a given set of genetic constraints, is therefore a condition of survival. In animals, non-genetic adaptations depends chiefly upon blind physiological and behavioral adjustments to environmental circumstances, for example as by hibernation; animals can also adapt by manipulating their environments, as exemplified by beaver dams or fox holes. In man, these instinctive biological responses to environmental changes are richly supplemented by creative adaptations resulting from deliberate choices.

Human behavior is governed in part by instincts which operate outside consciousness and free will. As in animals, these instincts come ready-made and enable the organism to deal in a specific and often successful manner with stereotyped life situations repeatedly experienced by the species during its evolutionary past. But precisely because instincts are so pointed and mechanical, they are of little if any use for adaptation to change; in particular they do not enable man to meet flexibly and creatively the unforeseeable and fluid complexities of his ever-changing physical and social environments. Whereas instincts stand for biological security, awareness and free will account for adventurous liberty and creativity. Henri Bergson in *Creative Evolution* (1907) and John Dewey in *Creative Intelli-*

gence (1917) emphasized that thought is the instrument which makes it possible for man to convert his adaptive responses into creative processes. Much of human creativity is indeed based on creative adaptations.

The word *adaptation* is commonly used by scientists in a purely deterministic sense to denote the kind of fitness that enables an organism to function and reproduce in a particular environment. This fitness is the outcome of processes amenable to traditional scientific explanations, such as those provided by knowledge of evolutionary development and of experiential conditioning. I shall first consider these deterministic aspects of adaptive processes, then discuss the reasons which make the present kind of scientific knowledge insufficient to account for creative adaptations in man.

The modern theory of biological adaptation began one century ago when Claude Bernard affirmed that the constancy of the internal environment is essential for the maintenance of free life. The final and most complete expression of Bernard's view on his topic is found in the "Leçons sur les phénomènes de la vie communs aux animaux et aux végétaux," first published in 1878-79. In Bernard's words, "The fixity of the *milieu intérieur* supposes a perfection of the organism such that the external variations are at each instant compensated for and equilibrated. Therefore, far from being indifferent to the external world, the higher animal is on the contrary constrained in a close and masterful *(savante)* relation with it, of such fashion that its equilibrium results from a continuous and delicate compensation established as if by the most sensitive of balances . . . . All of the vital mechanisms, however varied they may be, have always but one goal, to maintain the uniformity of the conditions of life in the internal environment." [18]

Bernard guessed that the maintenance of stable conditions in the body fluids and cells was in some way dependent upon neural control. He stated that "In the animal which has attained a completely independent life, the nervous system is called upon to achieve harmony among all these conditions." This view was first well-documented by W. B. Cannon's work on the ability of the sympathetic nervous system to maintain a constant internal equilibrium in the living body. Cannon's famous book *The Wisdom of the Body* constitutes a lucid extension of Bernard's view on the constancy of the *milieu intérieur,* and of homeostasis. [19]

A further elaboration of this concept, providing a link with cybernetics, was formulated by Norbert Wiener when he wrote, "Walter Cannon, going back to Claude Bernard, emphasized that the health and even the very existence of the body depends on what are called homeostatic processes . . . the apparent equilibrium of life is an equilibrium in which each deviation from the norm brings on a reaction in the opposite direction, which is of the nature of what we call negative feedback." [20] The recognition that feedback processes continuously operate in biological systems, and thus maintain them in a condition of dynamic equilibrium, has been one of the greatest creative forces in modern science. It pervades many areas of biology, ecology, and sociology.

In reality, most responses to environmental influences leave a permanent imprint on the system involved, thus chànging it irreversibly and imposing a direction on its further development. Living systems are characterized not by homeostasis, but by homokinesis. For example, homeostasis has been claimed to account for the stability of ecosystems; but the concept of ecological climax is a postulate which hardly ever fits reality. Final and stable ecological communities are exceptional in nature; ecological systems continuously change, even under natural conditions. Furthermore, any human intervention affects the course of ecological evolution. In many parts of the world, the primeval forest has been transformed by man into cultivated forests, or farmlands with different kinds of agricultural specialization, or even into moors as in Scotland and eastern England. Each one of these transformations has generated its own kind of ecological system, with its own evolutionary trend, and can thus be regarded as a form of creative adaptation.

There are also many examples of creative adaptation in social development. A feudal and agricultural country like Sweden was transformed within a century into a welfare urban society as a result of adaptive response to industrialization. Over most of the world, the homeostatic feedbacks of the supply and demand economy are giving way to new guided controls of socioeconomic systems.

In human biology, individual development proceeds step by step throughout life, in part as the unfolding of processes which are encoded in the genetic constitution, and also because the total environment has formative and repressive effects on the phenotypic expression of the genome. A century ago, Thomas Huxley asserted with his usual picturesque vigor that the newborn infant does not come into the world labeled scavenger or shopkeeper or bishop or duke; he is born as a mass of rather undifferentiated red pulp and it is only by educating him that we can discover his capabilities. As mentioned earlier, this concept applies not only to learning and behavioral characteristics but just as much to biological attributes.

The biological and psychological traits by which we know a person are not genetically determined; they correspond to phenotypic expressions and therefore illustrate the extent to which personality characteristics can be modified at will. Not only can normal development be so conditioned; but also reeducation can be designed to overcome disabilities resulting from certain pathological processes. It is certain that such reeducation involves more than passive training; it requires participation of the whole organism integrated through the mind for a truly creative process of adaptation. To repeat a statement made earlier, response is qualitatively different from reaction in that it implies an active participation of the person, usually with a creative outcome.

Following passively one's instincts is obviously easier than governing one's responses. But to be human means to be creative. Creation involves choices which often require painful mental effort; hence the worried features in human faces at the time of decisions concerning

57

the future.

In my book *Man Adapting* published in 1965, I developed the thesis that human life is shaped by three separate classes of determinants:

— the fundamental characteristics of man's biological and psychological nature which are essentially unchangeable because they emerged during evolutionary development and are inscribed in the genetic code;

— the environmental forces which each person experiences during his own life and to which he makes adaptive reactions and responses;

— and last but not least man's ability to choose among alternatives and to decide upon particular courses of action.

In the present lectures I have elected to emphasize the deliberate, creative aspects of adaptation because I believe that they best express the distinctive genius of the human species. Man is clearly differentiated from other animal species by the success of his creative adaptations.

I know of course that many illustrious scientists do not believe that it is intellectually justified to introduce such a vague and unproven concept as free will in the discussion of behavior; they try to account for human life as if it were the product of "Chance and Necessity" transcending "Freedom and Dignity." But while I admire these efforts as intellectual tours de force, I take them with a grain of salt. In fact, I tend to wonder with Northrop Frye whether they are not expressions of the "infantilism of specialists who see society as an extension of their own specialty." [21] I do not question of course that it is wise and profitable to learn as much as possible about human life through the abstractions that scientists derive from the experimental models they create. But I am of the opinion that it is also essential to continue accepting the evidence we derive from our senses and from our direct experiences.

In theory, all aspects of development and behavior are the expressions of biological forces. This deterministic philosophy can be legitimately summarized by the statement that individualism is the consequence of the interplay between the genotype and the total environment. But few are those among us who really believe that the orthodox concepts of determinism — as presently formulated — are sufficient to account for human life. The choices that each one of us makes determine the kind of experiences to which he is exposed and consequently give a direction to his further development. As a result, attitudes and attributes depend not only on purely biological forces but also on deliberate choices and on creative activities.

We must naturally take our limitations into account and accept the constraints of the physical world, but this acceptance is not incompatible with a creative attitude. Like Montaigne we must try to discover and express what is authentic about our own nature. "There is no one who, if he listens to himself, does not discover in himself a pattern all his own, a ruling pattern which struggles against education." To live according to this pattern gives us the opportunity to create "our great and glorious masterpiece . . . to compose our character is our duty." [22] Thoreau also expressed in *Walden* the belief that we must compose our own character:

Every man is the builder of a temple, called his body, to the god he worships, after a style purely his own, nor can he get off by hammering marble instead. We are all sculptors and painters, and our material is our own flesh and blood and bones. Any nobleness begins at once to refine a man's features, any meanness or sensuality to imbrute them.

The responsibility that each one of us has for his own evolution gives a rich and almost tragic significance to a statement made by Albert Camus in his novel *La Chute:* "Après un certain âge tout homme est responsable de son visage." (After a certain age every man is responsible for his own face.) H. L. Mencken attributes to E. M. Stanton the phrase "A man of fifty is responsible for his face." [23] And an almost identical statement appears as the very last entry in George Orwell's notebook, a few months before his death: "At 50, everyone has the face he deserves." [24] There could be no more absolute affirmation of belief in a person's ability to create his own life and character.

REFERENCES I

1. A. L. Vilakazi, review of *The Passing of Tribal Man in Africa*, P. C. W. Gutkind, ed., *American Anthropologist* 1972, 74, 858.

2. Barbara Ward, *Nationalism and Ideology* (New York: Norton, 1966), 21-27.

3. René Dubos, *A God Within* (New York: Scribner's, 1972).
   Clarence Glacken, *Traces on the Rhodian Shore* (Berkeley: Univ. of Calif. Press, 1967).
   Arnold Toynbee, *A Study of History I. Introduction and the Geneses of Civilizations* (London: Oxford, 1955).

4. A. H. Koller, *The Abbé DuBos* (Champaign, Ill.: Garrard Press, 1937).
   Glacken, *op. cit.*, 555.

5. E. Huntington, *The Character of Races as Influenced by Physical Environment, Natural Selection and Historical Development* (New York: Scribner's, 1924).

6. René Dubos, *Man Adapting* (New Haven: Yale Univ. Press, 1965), Chapter 2.

7. Quoted in Marc Bloch, *Feudal Society*, trans. L. A. Manyon, (Chicago: Univ. of Chicago Press, 1961), 148.

8. G. W. Lasker, ed., *The Processes of Ongoing Human Evolution* (Detroit: Wayne State Univ. Press, 1960).

9. Koller, *op. cit.*
   Glacken, *op. cit.*, 555.

10. Lynn White, Jr., *Machina ex Deo* (Cambridge, Mass.: MIT Press, 1968), 18.

11. Max Lerner, "Images of America and Man," *Graduate Journal*, III (1960), 22.

12. *Review of National Literatures: Russia — The Spirit of Nationalism*, 1972, 3, 247.

13. *Ibid.*, Rosette C. Lamont, "Solzhenitsyn's 'Maimed Oak',"
    153-182.

14. Edward H. Spices, "Persistent Cultural Systems," *Science,*
    1971, *174,* 795-800.

15. George Steiner, *In Bluebeard's Castle* (New Haven:
    Yale Univ. Press, 1971), 3.

16. A. Blok, quoted in *Review of National Literatures, op.
    cit.,* 140.

17. Robert Graves, "The Word Báraka," Blashfield Address,
    1962.

18. E. Vogt and E. Albert, eds., *People of Rimrock: A Study
    of Values in Five Cultures* (Cambridge: Harvard Univ.
    Press, 1966).

19. Clifford Geertz, "The Wet and the Dry: Traditional
    Irrigation in Bali and Morocco," *Human Ecology,* 1972,
    1, 23-40.

REFERENCES II

1. Trigant Burrow, *Preconscious Foundations of Human
   Experience* (New York: Basic Books, 1964), 124.

2. Jacquetta Hawkes, *Man on Earth* (New York: Random
   House, 1955), 186-87, 85.

3. Duns Scotus quoted in F. M. Bergounioux, "Notes on
   the Mentality of Primitive Man," in S. L. Washburn,
   ed., *Social Life of Early Man* (Chicago: Aldine Publishing Co., 1961), 112.

4. Maxim Gorky, quoted in Burrow, *op. cit.,* 114.

5. Norman Mailer, *Advertisements for Myself* (Berkley:
   Berkley Publishing, 196?) 304.

6. René Dubos, *So Human an Animal* (New York: Scribner's, 1968).